CW01024104

Managing for health and safety

HSE Books

Contents

Introduction

This book is mainly for leaders, owners, trustees and line managers. It will particularly help those who need to put in place or oversee their organisation's health and safety arrangements.

The advice may also help workers and their representatives, as well as health and safety practitioners and training providers.

How this book can help you

Organisations have a legal duty to put in place suitable arrangements to manage for health and safety. This book provides a framework to help you do that effectively, in a way that your organisation can tailor to your own circumstances.

In implementing your arrangements, you should consult with your employees or their representatives, including trade unions where they are recognised.

The framework described in this book is universal but how far action is needed will depend on the size and nature of the organisation, and the risks from its activities, products or services. The guidance is also available on HSE's 'Managing for health and safety' website at www.hse.gov.uk/managing.

If you need information on how to minimise particular risks in your organisation then 'The health and safety toolbox: How to control risks at work' will be helpful (www.hse.gov.uk/toolbox).

If you just need basic information or are getting started in managing for health and safety in your organisation, then the best place to look is 'Health and safety made simple: The basics for your business' (www.hse.gov.uk/simple-health-safety).

If you are a microbusiness, you can get information from the Federation of Small Businesses (www.fsb.org.uk).

How to use the book

This book will help you, as leaders, owners, trustees and line managers, put the right measures in place to manage the real risks to health and safety in your organisation.

Part 1 gives you the core elements of managing for health and safety and how they can fit with how you run the rest of your business.

Part 2 shows you what to look for when deciding if you're doing what you need to do.

Part 3 gives advice on delivering effective arrangements. It will be particularly useful to those who need to put in place or oversee their organisation's arrangements for health and safety, eg health and safety managers.

Part 4 signposts resources from HSE and other organisations. There are also short 'Find out more' lists with relevant sources of advice throughout the book.

The Plan, Do, Check, Act approach

HSE has moved away from using the POPMAR (Policy, Organising, Planning, Measuring performance, Auditing and Review) model of managing health and safety to a 'Plan, Do, Check, Act' approach.

The move towards Plan, Do, Check, Act achieves a balance between the systems and behavioural aspects of management.

It also treats health and safety management as an integral part of good management generally, rather than as a stand-alone system.

The high-level descriptions may vary, depending on the industry or sector you are working in, but a summary of the actions involved in delivering effective arrangements and how they are frequently described is given in Table 1, under the headings of Plan, Do, Check, Act.

Table 1 The read-across between Plan, Do, Check, Act and other management systems

Plan, Do, Check, Act	Conventional health and safety management	Process safety
Plan	Determine your policy/Plan for implementation	Define and communicate acceptable performance and resources needed
Do	Profile risks/Organise for health and safety/ Implement your plan	Identify and assess risks/Identify controls/ Record and maintain process safety knowledge
		Implement and manage control measures
Check	Measure performance (monitor before events, investigate after events)	Measure and review performance/Learn from measurements and findings of investigations
Act	Review performance/Act on lessons learned	

Plan

- Think about where you are now and where you need to be.
- Say what you want to achieve, who will be responsible for what, how you will achieve your aims, and how you will measure your success. You may need to write down this policy and your plan to deliver it.
- Decide how you will measure performance. Think about ways to do this that go beyond looking at accident figures; look for leading indicators as well as lagging indicators. These are also called active and reactive indicators (see 'Types of monitoring' on page 41).
- Consider fire and other emergencies. Co-operate with anyone who shares your workplace and co-ordinate plans with them.
- Remember to plan for changes and identify any specific legal requirements that apply to you.

Do

- **Identify your risk profile**
  - Assess the risks, identify what could cause harm in the workplace, who it could harm and how, and what you will do to manage the risk.
  - Decide what the priorities are and identify the biggest risks.
- **Organise your activities to deliver your plan**
  In particular, aim to:
  - Involve workers and communicate, so that everyone is clear on what is needed and can discuss issues – develop positive attitudes and behaviours.
  - Provide adequate resources, including competent advice where needed.
- **Implement your plan**
  - Decide on the preventive and protective measures needed and put them in place.
  - Provide the right tools and equipment to do the job and keep them maintained.
  - Train and instruct, to ensure everyone is competent to carry out their work.
  - Supervise to make sure that arrangements are followed.

Check

- **Measure your performance**
  - Make sure that your plan has been implemented – 'paperwork' on its own is not a good performance measure.
  - Assess how well the risks are being controlled and if you are achieving your aims. In some circumstances formal audits may be useful.
- **Investigate the causes of accidents, incidents or near misses**

Act

- **Review your performance**
  - Learn from accidents and incidents, ill-health data, errors and relevant experience, including from other organisations.
  - Revisit plans, policy documents and risk assessments to see if they need updating.
- **Take action on lessons learned, including from audit and inspection reports**

Figure 1 The Plan, Do, Check, Act cycle

Plan, Do, Check, Act should not be seen as a once-and-for-all action. You may need to go round the cycle more than once, particularly when:

- starting out;
- developing a new process, product or service; or
- implementing any change.

Part 1: Core elements of managing for health and safety

Organisations have a legal duty to put in place suitable arrangements to manage for health and safety. As this can be viewed as a wide-ranging, general requirement HSE encourages a common-sense and practical approach. It should be part of the everyday process of running an organisation and an integral part of workplace behaviours and attitudes.

Whatever your industry, or the size or nature of your organisation, the keys to effectively managing for health and safety are:

■ leadership and management (including appropriate business processes);
■ a trained/skilled workforce;
■ an environment where people are trusted and involved.

HSE advocates that all of these elements, underpinned by an understanding of the profile of risks the organisation creates or faces, are needed. This links back to wider risk management and can be pictured in Figure 2 at the top of page 5.

Successful delivery can rarely be achieved by one-off interventions. A sustained and systematic approach is necessary. This may not require a formal health and safety management system but, whatever approach is used, it probably contains the steps Plan, Do, Check, Act. However, the success of whatever process or system is in place hinges on the attitudes and behaviours of people in the organisation.

Figure 2 The core elements

Legal duties

All organisations have management processes or arrangements to deal with payroll, personnel issues, finance and quality control – managing health and safety is no different.

The Management of Health and Safety at Work Regulations 1999 require employers to put in place arrangements to control health and safety risks. As a minimum, you should have the processes and procedures required to meet the legal requirements, including:

■ a written health and safety policy (if you employ five or more people);
■ assessments of the risks to employees, contractors, customers, partners, and any other people who could be affected by your activities – and record the significant findings in writing (if you employ five or more people). Any risk assessment must be 'suitable and sufficient';

■ arrangements for the effective planning, organisation, control, monitoring and review of the preventive and protective measures that come from risk assessment;
■ access to competent health and safety advice, for example see the Occupational Safety and Health Consultants Register (OSHCR) at www.hse.gov.uk/oshcr;
■ providing employees with information about the risks in your workplace and how they are protected;
■ instruction and training for employees in how to deal with the risks;
■ ensuring there is adequate and appropriate supervision in place;
■ consulting with employees about their risks at work and current preventive and protective measures.

Risk profiling

Effective leaders and line managers know the risks their organisations face, rank them in order of importance and take action to control them. The range of risks goes beyond health and safety risks to include quality, environmental and asset damage, but issues in one area could impact in another.

Although you may not use these precise terms, you will most likely have built a risk profile that covers:

- the nature and level of the risks faced by your organisation;
- the likelihood of adverse effects occurring and the level of disruption;
- the costs associated with each type of risk;
- the effectiveness of the controls in place to manage those risks.

Find out more

For more advice on risk profiling see page 8 and pages 21–4.

Management of Health and Safety at Work Regulations 1999: www.legislation.gov.uk/uksi/1999/3242/contents/made

HSE provides advice and templates on these processes – see our risk management site for more information (www.hse.gov.uk/risk).

Health and safety management systems

A formal management system or framework can help you manage health and safety; it's your decision whether to use one or not. Examples include:

- national and international standards such as:
  - BS OHSAS 18001 *Occupational health and safety management systems*;
  - BS EN ISO 9001 *Quality management system*;
- in-house standards, procedures or codes;
- sector-specific frameworks such as:
  - the Energy Institute's *High-level framework for process safety management*;
  - the Chemical Industries Association *Responsible Care* framework.

Although the language and methodology vary, the key actions can usually be traced back to Plan, Do, Check, Act (see the summary on pages 2–3).

Documentation

Keep health and safety documents functional and concise, with the emphasis on their effectiveness rather than sheer volume of paperwork.

Focusing too much on the formal documentation of a health and safety management system will distract you from addressing the human elements of its implementation – the focus becomes the process of the system itself rather than actually controlling risks.

Attitudes and behaviours

Effectively managing for health and safety is not just about having a management or safety management system. The success of whatever process or system is in place still hinges on the attitudes and behaviours of people in the organisation (this is sometimes referred to as the 'safety culture').

Find out more

See Part 2 for examples of positive and negative health and safety attitudes, and situations where there may be underlying cultural issues.

British Standards can be obtained in PDF or hard-copy formats from BSI: http://shop.bsigroup.com

Energy Institute's *High-level framework for process safety management*: www.energyinst.org/eipss

Chemical Industries Association: www.cia.org.uk

Part 2: Are you doing what you need to do?

This part of the book gives you, as leaders, owners, trustees and line managers, examples of evidence to look for when deciding if you are doing what you need to do to manage for health and safety effectively. It will help you answer fundamental questions such as:

■ What are the strengths and weaknesses of your organisation's health and safety performance, and are there any barriers to change?
■ How reliable and sustainable for the future are the measures currently in place?
■ If your organisation is getting risk control right, why is that? For example, does performance depend on one person's dedication and enthusiasm or is it a key value across the organisation?

■ If there are problems, what are the underlying reasons, eg competence, resources, accountability, lack of engagement with the workforce?
■ Have you learned from situations where things have gone wrong?

The advice also reflects the areas that the health and safety regulator will consider when assessing the effectiveness of your arrangements.

The examples in the following pages with key areas of 'What it looks like when done effectively' indicate positive health and safety attitudes and behaviours. On the other hand, the examples also cover facets of 'What it looks like when done badly or not at all' as this could indicate underlying cultural issues.

Risk profiling

The risk profile of an organisation informs all aspects of the approach to leading and managing its health and safety risks.

Every organisation will have its own risk profile. This is the starting point for determining the greatest health and safety issues for the organisation. In some businesses the risks will be tangible and immediate safety hazards, whereas in other organisations the risks may be health-related and it may be a long time before the illness becomes apparent.

A risk profile examines:

- the nature and level of the threats faced by an organisation;
- the likelihood of adverse effects occurring;
- the level of disruption and costs associated with each type of risk;
- the effectiveness of controls in place to manage those risks.

The outcome of risk profiling will be that the right risks have been identified and prioritised for action, and minor risks will not have been given too much priority. It also informs decisions about what risk control measures are needed.

Find out more

For small/medium businesses and those new to health and safety: *Health and safety made simple: The basics for your business* Leaflet INDG449 HSE Books
www.hse.gov.uk/pubns/indg449.htm
Microsite: www.hse.gov.uk/simple-health-safety

For larger/more mature businesses: *The health and safety toolbox: How to control risks at work* HSG268 HSE Books ISBN 978 0 7176 6587 7
www.hse.gov.uk/pubns/books/hsg268.htm
Microsite: www.hse.gov.uk/toolbox

British Standard BS 31100:2008 *Risk management: Code of practice* http://shop.bsigroup.com

Leading and managing for health and safety

'There is a need for a sensible and proportionate approach to risk management, in short, a balanced approach – this means ensuring that paperwork is proportionate, does not get in the way of doing the job, and it certainly does not mean risk elimination at all costs.'

Judith Hackitt, HSE Chair

Leaders, at all levels, need to understand the range of health and safety risks in their part of the organisation and to give proportionate attention to each of them. This applies to the level of detail and effort put into assessing the risks, implementing controls, supervising and monitoring.

What are you doing?

Leading for health and safety
- Is there leadership from the top of your organisation? Is it visible?
- What example do you set? Do you talk about health and safety? When did you last do this?
- What are your significant risks and how do you know they are being controlled?
- Are the health and safety implications of your business decisions recognised and addressed?
- Is there evidence that the board or leader of your organisation is responsive to the health and safety information that is reported?

Management tasks
- How is health and safety included in the processes or management arrangements you have for running the business?
- Are the health and safety responsibilities of key people set out, for example:
  - Who is the champion/focus at the board?
  - Who sets policy and standards?
  - Who monitors performance?
  - Are these responsibilities reflected in their job descriptions?
- How do you ensure access to competent advice?
- How do you ensure health and safety information is communicated effectively within and beyond your organisation?
- How do you control your contractors?
- How do you review your health and safety performance?

Table 2 Leading and managing for health and safety – what to look for

Use the following examples of effective and ineffective health and safety management to check if you are doing what you need to do on leadership.

What it looks like when done effectively	What it looks like when done badly or not at all
Leaders ■ Maintain attention on the significant risks and implementation of adequate controls. ■ Demonstrate their commitment by their actions; they are aware of the key health and safety issues. ■ Ensure consultation with the workforce on health and safety. ■ Challenge unsafe behaviour in a timely way.	**Leaders** ■ Set no health and safety priorities. ■ Don't understand the need to maintain oversight. ■ Don't meet their own organisation's standards/procedures, eg wearing correct PPE on site/shop floor. ■ Lack of engagement with health and safety by workers. ■ Health and safety is seen as an add-on, irrelevance or nuisance. ■ Poor incident history (accidents, near misses, plant damage or other indicators, eg poor maintenance, poor housekeeping).
Management of health and safety ■ A systematic approach is used to manage health and safety. ■ People understand the risks and control measures associated with their work. ■ Contractors adhere to the same standards. ■ Appropriate documentation is available: current, organised, relevant. ■ People understand their roles and those of others. ■ Performance is measured – to check controls are working and standards are being implemented, and to learn from mistakes after things go wrong.	**Management of health and safety** ■ Incomplete or missing paperwork. Does not link to actual risks in workplace. ■ Confusion over roles, inaction as no one takes responsibility for health and safety, distrust of management motives. ■ Widespread, routine violations of procedures. No oversight of contractors. ■ Information is not passed on, not understood, or not implemented. ■ Managers are unaware of employee concerns or do not respond appropriately. ■ Lessons are never learned.
Beyond compliance ■ If a formal system (such as BS OHSAS 18001, ISO 9001) is used, has it been externally certified – is the certification accredited? ■ Health and safety is integrated into business processes. ■ Benchmarking is used to compare performance with others. ■ Supply chains are influenced to improve health and safety. ■ A 'wellness' programme is in place.	

Managing for health and safety

Additional factors to consider

Board members or directors
■ Joint advice from HSE and the Institute of Directors will help you set your agenda for effective leadership of health and safety (see the leaflet in 'Find out more' below).

Smaller and medium-sized businesses
■ A formal, documented system is not always necessary.
■ The behaviours and attributes of a very small group, or perhaps one person such as the business owner, are critical.
■ What the owner does to set an example and to provide a lead on health and safety to their staff determines the outcome.
■ Medium-sized enterprises can show a mix of the formal and informal when it comes to health and safety arrangements.

Larger organisations
■ Is there someone in senior management who champions health and safety on the board?
■ Who sets the organisational policy and standards and how are they monitored?
■ Does the board receive and act upon reports on health and safety matters?
■ What key performance indicators (KPIs) do you use to monitor health and safety performance?
■ Do you periodically review your arrangements for managing for health and safety in light of any organisational changes?

Process industries
■ Leadership on the key area of process safety is critical.
■ Board level involvement and competence are essential – constant and active engagement in, and promotion of, process safety by the leadership sets a positive safety culture – 'rigour in leadership'.
■ Key factors to address are:
  - How do you maintain corporate knowledge, overall technical leadership and competence?
  - How do you monitor process safety performance to ensure business risks are effectively managed?
  - Do you publish safety information to provide public assurance?

Managing occupational health issues
■ Dealing with a work-related ill-health issue in an organisation may not be as straightforward as it is for a safety issue. It is important to get the right competent advice to identify what needs to be done. Remember that you need to consider both immediate ill-health risks and those which can have a latency period before any ill health is seen.

■ Key occupational ill-health issues include diseases arising from exposure to asbestos, chemicals, biological agents, dusts, noise, manual handling and vibration.
■ Questions to ask:
  - Do I have an occupational ill-health problem in my business and have I taken steps to prevent ill health in my workforce?
  - Do my workers know which health risks in my business could affect them?

Find out more

There is more advice on leading and managing in Part 3.

Leading health and safety at work: Leadership actions for directors and board members Leaflet INDG417(rev1) HSE Books www.hse.gov.uk/pubns/indg417.htm

The TUC's 'Worksmart' website: www.worksmart.org.uk/health/questions.php

The IOSH website's 'Occupational health toolkit': www.iosh.co.uk

Competence

'Truly effective health and safety management requires competency across every facet of an organisation and through every level of the workforce.'

The health and safety of Great Britain: Be part of the solution (www.hse.gov.uk/strategy/document.htm)

Competence is the ability to undertake responsibilities and perform activities to a recognised standard on a regular basis. It combines practical and thinking skills, knowledge and experience.

The Management of Health and Safety at Work Regulations 1999 require an employer to appoint one or more competent people to help them implement the measures they need to take to comply with the legal requirements. That could be a member of the workforce, the owner/manager, or an external consultant. The competent person should focus on the significant risks and those with serious consequences.

The competence of individuals is vital, whether they are employers, managers, supervisors, employees or contractors, especially those with safety-critical roles (such as plant maintenance engineers). It ensures they recognise the risks in their activities and can apply the right measures to control and manage those risks.

What are you doing?

- Health and safety responsibilities of managers/ supervisors
  - How are they made aware of them?
  - What training have they been given to fulfil roles and responsibilities?
  - How are they held accountable?
  - Do they recognise continuing development needs, eg in annual appraisals?
- Who fulfils the role of health and safety competent person?
  - What are their background, training and qualifications?
  - What is their awareness of current health and safety law relating to key risks?
  - Are they allowed enough time to dedicate to health and safety?
- External provider of competent advice
  - How were they selected?
  - What is their competence to provide advice to this particular organisation?
  - Do they allocate adequate resources and tailor advice to this particular organisation?
  - Check that the documentation provided, eg visit reports, is suitable, covers the key hazards, assesses the right risks and gives the right advice.

- Does the organisation act upon advice from the competent person?
- If there is an identified lack of competence in a particular area, what are you doing to deal with the problem?
- How are staff selected for the tasks carried out?
- Are arrangements in place to ensure staff are aware of roles and responsibilities?
- Have you identified the training they need?
  - Ensure relevant and sufficient training is delivered. Look for use of training schedules, operating manuals, sampling delivery of training, training for trainers etc.
  - Check the necessary level of competence has been reached.
  - Check that training is applied.
  - Provide update/refresher training.
  - Ensure training records are kept.
- Have you provided enough competent cover for absences?

Table 3 Competence – what to look for

Use the following examples of effective and ineffective health and safety management to check if you are doing what you need to do on competence.

What it looks like when done effectively	What it looks like when done badly or not at all
<ul><li>All know the risks created by the business and understand how to manage them.</li><li>Key responsible people/job holders are identified and there are clearly established roles and responsibilities.</li><li>People have the necessary training, skills, knowledge and experience to fulfil their responsibilities and are given enough time to do so.</li><li>Training takes place during normal working hours and employees are not charged.</li></ul>**Beyond compliance**<ul><li>Lessons learned and good practice are shared internally and externally.</li></ul>	<ul><li>Lack of awareness of key hazards/risks.</li><li>People lack the skills, knowledge and experience to do their job.</li><li>Health and safety advice and training are irrelevant, incompetent or wrong.</li><li>No standards set; people not held accountable.</li><li>Insufficient action is taken to comply with the law.</li><li>Knee-jerk reactions follow incidents/near misses.</li><li>The organisation does not know what it needs to do to move forward.</li></ul>

Additional factors to consider

Smaller businesses
- In small businesses the responsibility of providing competent advice often rests with the owner/manager.
- An HSE leaflet *Getting specialist help with health and safety* will help you ask the right questions if you are looking for competent advice (see 'Find out more' below).

Larger organisations
- Who has the board lead on health and safety?
- What is their competence in, and awareness of, health and safety issues?
- Do they play an active part and how do they support the health and safety competent person?
- See the HSE competence-related guidance for a specific industry, task or working environment (www.hse.gov.uk/competence).

Process industries
- At least one board member should be technically competent in process safety management. The competence of plant maintenance engineers is also crucial.
- You can find more information in the joint HSE/Process Safety Leadership Group guidance on the *Principles of Process Safety Leadership*.

Find out more

There is more advice on competence in Part 3.

Management of Health and Safety at Work Regulations www.legislation.gov.uk/uksi/1999/3242/contents/made

Getting specialist help with health and safety Leaflet INDG420(rev1) HSE Books www.hse.gov.uk/pubns/indg420.htm

Principles of Process Safety Leadership HSE/Process Safety Leadership Group www.hse.gov.uk/comah/buncefield/pslgprinciples.htm

Worker consultation and involvement

'I find it hard to imagine how one could ever put in place an effective workplace health and safety system that did not include real participation and engagement of the workforce.'

Judith Hackitt, HSE Chair

The legal requirements for consultation and involvement of the workforce include:

- providing information;
- instruction;
- training;
- engaging in consultation with employees, and especially trade unions where they are recognised.

Beyond the required legal minimum standard, worker involvement is the full participation of the workforce in the management of health and safety.

At its most effective, full involvement creates a culture where relationships between employers and employees are based on collaboration, trust and joint problem solving. Employees are involved in assessing workplace risks and the development and review of workplace health and safety policies in partnership with the employer.

What are you doing?

- How are employees or their representatives consulted and involved in health and safety matters?
- How effective are those mechanisms in relation to the organisation's size and structure, or the rate of workplace change?
- Are the needs of any vulnerable workers (temporary or agency staff, or those whose first language is not English) appropriately met, including through, for example, the use of interpreters, use of symbols and diagrams rather than written instructions?
- Are employees consulted in good time?
- Do health and safety representatives have sufficient time and access to the facilities they need to carry out their functions?
- Do contractors have an appropriate level of induction and training?

Table 4 Worker consultation and involvement – what to look for

Use the following examples of effective and ineffective health and safety management to check if you are doing what you need to do on worker consultation and involvement.

What it looks like when done effectively	What it looks like when done badly or not at all

■ Instruction, information and training are provided to enable employees to work in a safe and healthy manner.
■ Safety representatives and representatives of employee safety carry out their full range of functions.
■ The workforce are consulted (either directly or through their representatives) in good time on issues relating to their health and safety and the results of risk assessments.
 	
Beyond compliance
 	
■ Feedback mechanisms exist for health and safety matters, such as:
  – 'suggestions boxes' or more formal open meetings with management;
  – team meetings are held and may be led by employees.
■ Joint decisions on health and safety are made between managers and workers.
	■ Employees lack the right level of information, instruction and training needed to do their job in a safe and healthy manner.
	■ Representatives cannot carry out their functions.
	■ Employees don't know who they would go to if they had health and safety concerns.
	■ Health and safety controls don't seem practical or employees are having to work around difficulties.
	■ Line managers don't discuss how to safely use new equipment or how to do a job safely.
	■ There is little or no evidence of information being cascaded through the organisation (eg team meetings, notice boards etc).

Additional factors to consider

Dynamic situations where the working environment changes regularly
■ Worker consultation and involvement is fundamental in ensuring risks are effectively managed.
■ How do you support the necessary increased emphasis on the workforce to work in a safe manner?

Smaller businesses
■ Smaller businesses tend to have simpler, less formal systems in place such as face-to-face discussion, toolbox talks, or periodic meetings on specific issues.
■ Do your arrangements allow employees to have a say?

Larger organisations
■ Larger organisations are likely to require or have some form of formal system of consultation, although informal systems may be present as well.
■ There should be effective consultation arrangements, including an appropriate number of health and safety representatives and representatives of employee safety, as well as safety committees and meetings for key issues such as organisational changes.

Find out more

There is more advice on worker consultation and involvement in Part 3.

HSE's worker involvement pages: www.hse.gov.uk/involvement

Consulting employees on health and safety: A brief guide to the law Leaflet INDG232(rev2) HSE Books www.hse.gov.uk/pubns/indg232.htm

Part 3: Delivering effective arrangements

This part of the book is for those who need to put in place their organisation's arrangements for health and safety or have particular responsibility for overseeing them.

The guidance will help you address any specific issues you have identified in answering the questions posed for leaders, owners, trustees and line managers in Part 2.

It does this by taking the Plan, Do, Check, Act framework, identifying the key actions needed in each part of that cycle and relating them back, where appropriate, to leadership, management, worker involvement and competence.

See Figure 1 on page 3 for a flowchart that illusrates the Plan, Do, Check, Act framework.

The key actions covered are:

Plan

- Determining your policy
- Planning for implementation

Do

- Profiling your health and safety risks
- Organising for health and safety
- Implementing your plan

Check

- Measuring performance
- Investigating accidents and incidents

Act

- Reviewing performance
- Learning lessons

PLAN

DO

ACT

CHECK

Planning

Policy

Content

Who should write it?

Consulting/acting on your policy

Planning is essential

Effective planning

PLAN
Policy
Planning

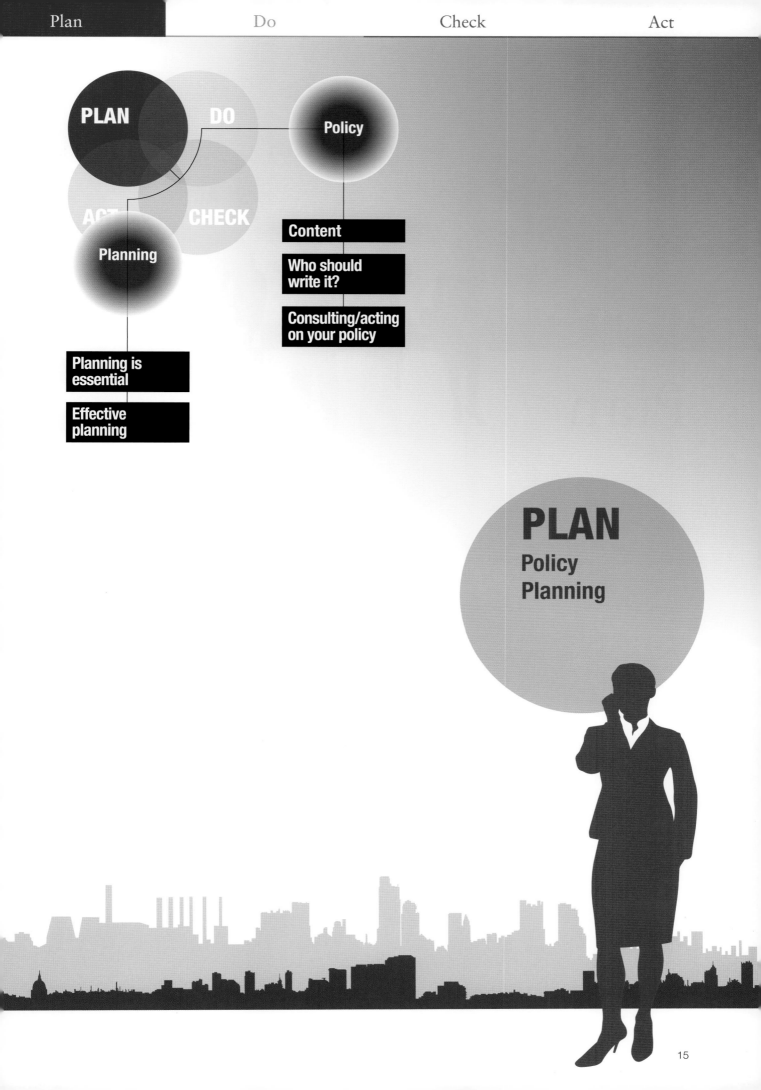

Plan

To implement your health and safety policy, you need to establish and maintain an effective health and safety management system that is proportionate to the risks.

You should set the direction for effective health and safety management, and a policy that sets a clear direction will help to ensure communication of health and safety duties and benefits throughout the organisation.

Policies should be designed to meet legal requirements, prevent health and safety problems, and enable you to respond quickly where difficulties arise or new risks are introduced.

- Think about where you are now and where you need to be.
- Say what you want to achieve, who will be responsible for what, how you will achieve your aims, and how you will measure your success. You may need to write down this policy and your plan to deliver it.
- Decide how you will measure performance. Think about ways to do this that go beyond looking at accident figures – look for leading and lagging indicators. These are also called active and reactive indicators (see 'Types of monitoring' on page 41).
- Consider fire and other emergencies. Co-operate with anyone who shares your workplace and co-ordinate plans with them.
- Remember to plan for changes and identify any specific legal requirements that apply to you.

Determining your policy

What should your policy cover?

An important part of achieving effective health and safety outcomes is having a strategy and making clear plans.

You need to think about what you are going to do to manage health and safety, then decide who is going to do what and how. This is your health and safety policy. If your organisation has five or more employees, that policy must be written down.

Your policy sets a clear direction for the organisation to follow and should be shared throughout the workforce, so that everyone understands how health and safety will be managed.

Who is best placed to write it?

It is best written by someone within the organisation rather than someone from outside, as it needs to reflect the organisation's:

- values and beliefs;
- commitment to provide a safe and healthy environment.

Consulting and acting on your policy

It should be written in consultation with the workforce, and should be signed by a person at the top of the organisation – the owner or a director. Most importantly, you should make sure your actions, and those of your workers, mirror the statements you have made.

Find out more

HSE have created a basic template to help you develop your policy:
www.hse.gov.uk/simple-health-safety/write.htm

Planning for implementation

Why planning is essential

Planning is essential for the implementation of health and safety policies. Adequate control of risk can only be achieved through co-ordinated action by all members of the organisation. An effective system for health and safety management requires organisations to plan to:

- control risks;
- react to changing demands;
- sustain positive health and safety attitudes and behaviours.

Effective planning

Effective planning is concerned with prevention through identifying and controlling risks. This is especially important when dealing with health risks that may only become apparent after a long period of time.

In addition to setting your policy, planning should include steps to ensure legal compliance and procedures for dealing with emergency situations. It should involve people throughout the organisation.

Planning the system you will use to manage health and safety involves:

- designing, developing and implementing suitable and proportionate management arrangements, risk control systems and workplace precautions;
- operating and maintaining the system while also seeking improvement where needed;
- linking it to how you manage other aspects of the organisation.

In order to plan successfully, you need to establish:

- where the organisation is now, by considering accurate information about the current situation;
- where you need to be, using legal requirements and benchmarking to make comparisons;
- what action is necessary to reach that point.

Key actions in effective policy development and planning

Leaders

- Make a statement of intention. Say what you will do to keep a safe and healthy environment for your workers and anyone else who could be affected by your work activities.
- Clearly set out everyone's roles and responsibilities. Include those with particular roles, for example directors, supervisors/managers, safety representatives, workers, fire wardens, first-aiders and the competent person.
- Say how things will be done and what resources will be allocated to make things happen. Include details of the systems and procedures that will be in place to help to meet your legal obligations, such as:
  - how risk assessments will be carried out;
  - what your plans are for training and safe use of equipment;
  - what controls you will have in place to ensure your specifiers and buyers are competent in assessing the risks in procurement, for example they know the requirements for purchasing suitable personal protective equipment (PPE);
  - how accidents/incidents will be investigated;
  - how workers will be consulted;
  - how equipment will be maintained;
  - how you will measure the success of your plan.
- Consider how you will measure health and safety performance. Will there be performance targets, for example reductions in accidents or absences, or an increase in reporting issues or near misses?
- Prioritise actions.
- Sign the policy statement to demonstrate commitment to health and safety.

Managers

- Think about management of contractors when developing a policy, if this is relevant to your organisation.
- Identify when you will revisit your policy and plans, for example:
  - when changes have taken place, such as in processes or staff;
  - following accident or incident investigations, both within the organisation and where lessons have been learned from others;
  - following consultation with employees' representatives;
  - if you receive new information, eg from manufacturers or others in the same sector or industry.
- Talk to other occupants not employed or managed by you, but who share the same premises.

Worker consultation and involvement

- Discuss your plans with workers or their representatives.
- Communicate the plan so that everyone knows what is required.

Competence

- When developing plans and policies, consider the level of competence necessary to comply with the law.

PLAN DO CHECK

Risk profiling

Implementing your plan

Organising

Assessing the risks

What the law says

The key steps

Documentation

Implementing risk control plans

Controls and supervisors

Managing contractors

Co-operation

Involving workers

Contacts with external services

Emergency procedures and planning

Communication

Size and structure

Competence

Competent person

Capabilities and training

Specialist help

Assessing the level of risk

Risk controls

Recording your findings

Health surveillance

DO
Risk profiling
Organising
Implementing your plan

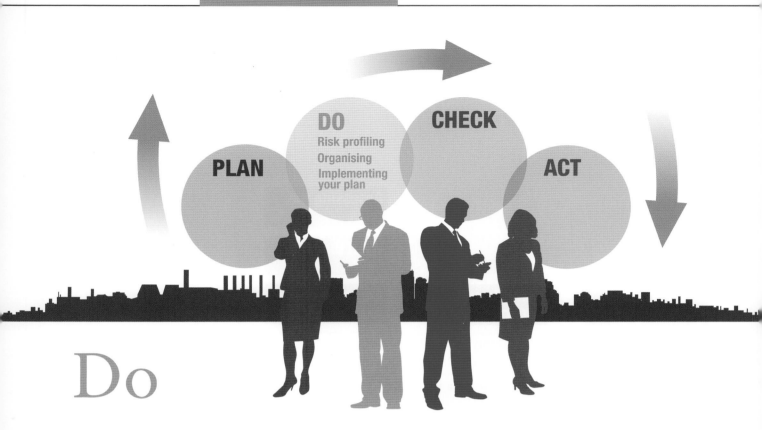

Do

Delivery depends on an effective management system to ensure, so far as reasonably practicable, the health and safety of employees and other people affected by your work.

Organisations should aim to protect people by introducing management systems and practices that ensure risks are dealt with sensibly, responsibly and proportionately.

- **Profiling your organisation's health and safety risks**
  - Assess the risks, identify what could cause harm in the workplace, who it could harm and how, and what you will do to manage the risk.
  - Decide what the priorities are and identify the biggest risks.

- **Organising for health and safety**
  In particular, aim to:
  - involve workers and communicate, so that everyone is clear on what is needed and can discuss issues – develop positive attitudes and behaviours;
  - provide adequate resources, including competent advice where needed.

- **Implementing your plan**
  - Decide on the preventive and protective measures needed and put them in place.
  - Provide the right tools and equipment to do the job and keep them maintained.
  - Train and instruct, to ensure everyone is competent to carry out their work.
  - Supervise to make sure that arrangements are followed.

What does 'so far as reasonably practicable' mean?

This means balancing the level of risk against the measures needed to control the real risk in terms of money, time or trouble. However, you do not need to take action if it would be grossly disproportionate to the level of risk.

Profiling your organisation's health and safety risks

Effective leaders and line managers know the risks their organisations face, rank them in order of importance and take action to control them.

The range of risks goes beyond health and safety risks to include quality, environmental and asset damage, but issues in one area could impact in another. For example, unsafe forklift truck driving may have a service or quality dimension as a result of damage to goods.

A risk profile examines the nature and levels of threats faced by an organisation. It examines the likelihood of adverse effects occurring, the level of disruption and costs associated with each type of risk and the effectiveness of the control measures in place.

Although you may not use these precise terms, you will most likely have built a risk profile that covers:

- the nature and level of the risks faced by your organisation;
- the likelihood of adverse effects occurring and the level of disruption;
- costs associated with each type of risk;
- effectiveness of the controls in place to manage those risks.

Assessing the risks

What types of risks need to be considered?

In some organisations the health and safety risks will be tangible and immediate safety issues, eg machine guarding, whereas in others the risks may be health-related and it could be a long time before the illness becomes apparent. Degrading plant integrity could also lead to later emerging risks in some businesses.

Health and safety risks also range from things that happen very infrequently but with catastrophic effects (high-hazard, low-frequency events, such as an oil refinery explosion) to things that happen much more frequently but with lesser consequences (low-hazard, high-frequency events). Clearly, the high-hazard, low-frequency example could destroy the business and would be high-priority in a risk profile.

Who should do the assessment?

A risk assessment should be completed by someone with a knowledge of the activity, process or material that is being assessed. Workers and their safety representatives are a valuable source of information.

If an adviser or consultant assists with the risk assessment, managers and workers should still be involved.

Who could be affected?

Consider all your activities, taking account of possible harm to:

- employees;
- contractors;
- members of the public;
- those using products and services;
- anyone else affected by the activity, such as neighbours.

Remember to think of how a risk could affect different groups, such as young or inexperienced workers, pregnant workers, workers with a disability, migrant workers or ageing workers. Also consider your supply chain – if that is not properly managed, the actions of others in those networks can impact on your health and safety risks.

What the law says on assessing risks

The law states that a risk assessment must be 'suitable and sufficient', ie it should show that:

- a proper check was made;
- you asked who might be affected;
- you dealt with all the obvious significant risks, taking into account the number of people who could be involved;
- the precautions are reasonable, and the remaining risk is low;
- you involved your workers or their representatives in the process.

The level of detail in a risk assessment should be proportionate to the risk and appropriate to the nature of the work. Insignificant risks can usually be ignored, as can risks arising from routine activities associated with life in general, unless the work activity compounds or significantly alters those risks.

Your risk assessment should only include what you could reasonably be expected to know – you are not expected to anticipate unforeseeable risks.

Find out more

HSE's risk assessment website: www.hse.gov.uk/risk

Management of Health and Safety at Work Regulations: www.legislation.gov.uk/uksi/1999/3242/contents/made

Assessing the level of risk

The level of risk arising from the work activity should determine how sophisticated the risk assessment needs to be.

Small businesses

For small businesses, with few or simple risks, a suitable and sufficient risk assessment can be a very straightforward process based on informed judgement and using appropriate guidance.

Medium-sized businesses or those with greater risks

In these cases, the risk assessment will need to be more sophisticated. You may need specialist advice for some areas of the assessment, for example:

- risks requiring specialist knowledge, eg a particularly complex process or technique;
- risks needing specialist analytical techniques, eg being able to measure air quality and to assess its impact.

Large and high-hazard sites

These sites will require the most developed and sophisticated risk assessments.

For manufacturing sites using or storing bulk hazardous substances, large-scale mineral extraction or nuclear plant, the risk assessment will be a significant part of the legally required safety case or report, and may incorporate such techniques as quantified risk assessment.

Other statutory requirements, eg the Control of Major Accident Hazards Regulations (COMAH) and nuclear installations licensing arrangements, include more specific and detailed arrangements for risk assessment.

Risk controls

When considering risk controls, discuss the issues with your workers and think about what is already being done, then compare it with the industry standard. For example, this could be industry-specific advice from HSE, an employer body, a trade association, a trade union or a safety organisation.

The risk assessment might have to concentrate more on the broad range of risks that can be foreseen:

- where the nature of the work may change fairly frequently or the workplace itself changes and develops (such as a construction site);
- where workers move from site to site.

Recording your findings

Record the significant findings. These should include a record of the preventive and protective measures in place to control the risks, and what further action, if any, needs to be taken to reduce risk sufficiently, for example health surveillance (see page 23).

If you have fewer than five employees you don't have to write anything down.

Find out more

More advice for small or low-risk businesses: *Health and safety made simple: The basics for your business* Leaflet INDG449 HSE Books www.hse.gov.uk/pubns/indg449.htm Microsite: www.hse.gov.uk/simple-health-safety

More advice on medium-sized businesses or those with greater risks: *The health and safety toolbox: How to control risks at work* HSG268 HSE Books ISBN 978 0 7176 6587 7 www.hse.gov.uk/pubns/books/hsg268.htm Microsite: www.hse.gov.uk/toolbox

More advice on large and high-hazard sites: HSE website on the Control of Major Accident Hazards Regulations (COMAH): www.hse.gov.uk/comah

Health surveillance

The risk assessment will identify circumstances in which health surveillance is required by specific health and safety regulations, eg the Control of Substances Hazardous to Health Regulations 2002 (COSHH).

Health surveillance should also be introduced where the assessment shows all the following criteria apply:

- there is an identifiable disease or adverse health condition related to the work concerned;
- valid techniques are available to detect indications of the disease or condition;
- there is a reasonable likelihood that the disease or condition may occur under the particular conditions of the work;
- surveillance is likely to help protect the health and safety of the employees to be covered.

Find out more

HSE's COSHH site: www.hse.gov.uk/coshh

HSE's health surveillance site: www.hse.gov.uk/health-surveillance

Key actions in effective risk profiling

Leaders

- Identify who takes ownership of health and safety risks:
  - This might be the owner, or chief executive – in larger organisations it may be a risk committee or a senior board champion for health and safety.
- Think about the consequences of the worst possible occurrence for your organisation:
  - How confident are you that plans are in place to control the effects?
- Ensure that risk assessments are carried out by a competent person:
  - This is someone who has the necessary skills, knowledge and experience to manage health and safety effectively.
- Maintain an overview of the risk-profiling process:
  - Make sure you are aware of the major risks within your organisation.
  - Check that minor risks have not been given too much priority and that major risks have not been overlooked.
- Identify who will be responsible for implementing risk controls and over what timescale.
- Remember to assess the effects of changing technology:
  - Think about issues related to changes in asset ownership. This may increase the risk profile if design information and knowledge haven't been passed on.
  - Have the effects of ageing plant and equipment been examined?

Managers

Identify the risks
- Identify the health and safety risks from the business and prioritise them. Think about the severity of the harm and the likelihood of occurrence. Concentrate on priority risks.
- Ensure that risks are owned so that appropriate resources can be allocated.
- Consider whether other risks are due to health and safety lapses.

Who might be affected?
- Think about everyone who might be affected by your work activities. Remember that certain groups may be at increased risk, eg young or inexperienced workers, pregnant workers, workers with a disability, migrant workers or ageing workers.

Control measures
- Consider whether any control measures are already in place or if further action is needed.
- Recognise that full implementation of control measures may take time, and implement interim measures to minimise the risks. ▶

▶ *Report, record and review*
- Report risk control performance regularly internally and consider whether it should be done externally.
- Make sure paperwork is kept to the minimum levels necessary. You only need to record the risk assessment if you employ five or more people.
- Review the organisation's risk profile regularly. Change within the organisation will affect the risk profile, eg during economic cycles such as recession and recovery, when there is an increase in workload, or when experience levels drop.

Worker consultation and involvement
- Do workers understand the organisation's risk profile?
  - Do they have the necessary information, instruction and training to deal with the risks that have been identified?
- Consult with workers and their representatives in all parts of the organisation to ensure that all areas of risk have been identified.

Competence
- A broad knowledge of the entire organisation will be needed to draw up its risk profile.
- In high-hazard organisations, identify what specialist advice may be necessary to identify hazards and analyse the risks.
- Make sure workers are trained and have information about risk controls.

Organising for health and safety

'Organising for health and safety' is the collective label given to activities in four key areas that together promote positive health and safety outcomes:

- **Controls within the organisation: the role of supervisors** – leadership, management, supervision, performance standards, instruction, motivation, accountability, rewards and sanctions
  - Managing contractors – anyone engaging contractors has health and safety responsibilities, both for the contractors and anyone else that could be affected by their activities
- **Co-operation** – between workers, their representatives and managers through active consultation and involvement
- **Communication** – across the whole organisation, through visible behaviour, written material and face-to-face discussion
- **Competence** – of individuals through recruitment, selection, training, coaching, specialist advice and avoiding complacency
  - Capabilities and training – help people gain the skills and knowledge, and ultimately the competence, to carry out their work safely and without risk to their health
  - Specialist help – you may need specialist help if your business has hazardous or complex processes

Controls within the organisation: the role of supervisors

The actions of leaders, line managers and supervisors are all important in delivering effective control of health and safety risks. Those actions are covered in 'Are you doing what you need to do?' (Part 2 of the book). This section complements that by focusing on supervisors.

Organisations will decide their own approach to supervision. Whatever method of supervision is used, the role of a supervisor or team leader is important in implementing effective controls.

Because of the regular contact they have with workers, they can make an important contribution to making sure:

- everyone knows how to work safely and without risk to their health;
- all workers follow the organisation's rules.

A supervisor can coach, help or guide workers to become and remain competent in these areas as well as others.

Key actions in supervising for health and safety effectively

Leaders

- Define supervisors' roles and responsibilities, and make sure they are trained and competent in carrying out their role, recognising the importance of supervision as a part of risk control.
- Make sure the supervisor/team leader has sufficient resources to deal with health and safety issues as part of 'getting the job done'.

Managers

- Consider the level of supervision necessary for each task according to its complexity and level of risk. Recognise that differing levels of supervision may be needed at certain times, for example during shift changeover or where there are young or inexperienced workers.
- Include supervisors in assessing risks and managing the effects of any changes.
- Encourage supervisors/line managers to have a positive attitude to health and safety – they should lead by example and encourage safe systems of work.
- Make sure supervisors understand the job, so they can make effective, safe decisions.
- This includes checking that they understand what is expected of them, especially during an emergency.
- Confirm that supervisors have planned the work and allocated sufficient resources to allow tasks to be completed safely and without risks to health.
- Make sure that a good example is being set for the workers, and that supervisors enforce the rules.
- If more than one supervisor/line manager is involved in a process, make sure that communication, co-ordination and co-operation take place.

Worker consultation and involvement

- Supervisors can help involve workers and their representatives:
  - by facilitating discussions on the likely risks in their work and precautions they should take;
  - in the introduction of any measures that may affect their health and safety.

Competence

- Supervisors must be competent to supervise the workers, and know the critical safety aspects of the job.

Managing contractors

Anyone engaging contractors has health and safety responsibilities, both for the contractors and anyone else that could be affected by their activities. Contractors themselves also have legal health and safety responsibilities. Make sure everyone understands the part they need to play in ensuring health and safety.

Use of contractors in itself does not result in poor health and safety standards, but poor management can lead to injuries, ill health, additional costs and delays. Working closely with the contractor will reduce the risks to your own employees and the contractors themselves.

Remember that contractors may be at particular risk; they may be strangers to your workplace and therefore unfamiliar with your organisation's procedures, rules, hazards and risks. Even regular contractors may need

reminding. The level of control needed will, of course, be proportionate to the complexity of the task.

On sites with major accident hazards, consider turnarounds and span of control – given the potentially very high numbers of contractors on-site (compared with the numbers in routine operations).

Find out more
Using contractors: A brief guide Leaflet INDG368(rev1)
HSE Books www.hse.gov.uk/pubns/indg368.htm

Managing health and safety in construction.
Construction (Design and Management) Regulations
2007. Approved Code of Practice L144
HSE Books ISBN 978 0 7176 6223 4
www.hse.gov.uk/pubns/books/l144.htm

Key actions in managing contractors effectively

Leaders

- Be clear about the work you expect the contractor to do and think about the standards of competence that will be required.
- Think carefully about contingencies if things don't go to plan.
- Demonstrate the importance your organisation places on health and safety in the selection of contractors.
- Ensure short cuts are not taken to reduce costs and there is no conflict of performance versus safety.
- Allocate sufficient time and resources to the job – in planning, preparing and carrying out the task.
- Support management decisions to stop work if there are serious health and safety concerns.
- Be ready to address health and safety failings by engaging directly with the leader of the contracting organisation, and acknowledge successes.

Managers

Monitor the contractor's health and safety performance
- Consider how the work will be managed and supervised before the work starts.
- Obtain the contractor's health and safety plans.
- Hold a pre-start meeting to ensure co-ordination and communication – ensure that incorrect assumptions are not made. Will the contractor need a site induction before beginning work on your site?
- Include contractor's activities in all inspections and checks.
- Hold regular progress meetings and raise health and safety issues as they occur.

Carry out a joint risk assessment of the work with the contractor
- Remember that some of the risks in your workplace may not be obvious to the contractor.
- Tell the contractor about any specific risks within your workplace, eg the presence of asbestos.
- Share method statements or safe systems of work.
- Tell employees and contractors about the risks, and make sure that the contractors let you know of any additional risks they will be introducing to your site.

Have the right procedures in place
- Ensure safe systems that are documented are carried out in practice.
- Make sure everyone is competent to carry out the tasks and that contractors receive induction.
- Make sure isolation procedures for machinery and plant are clear.

If you have an incident
- Stop the work if there are serious health and safety concerns.
- Investigate and address the root cause of any incident, feeding back results of the investigation to everyone involved.

Check that everyone understands the risks
- Ensure that work does not start until the contractors fully understand the risks and measures to control them.
- Make sure contractors understand the information, instruction and training you are giving them, taking account of any language difficulties or disabilities. You may need to provide information in a language other than English.

Worker consultation and involvement

- All workers should have clear lines of communication to report concerns.
- Communicate and co-ordinate so that employees and contractors know what is expected of them and when, and everyone understands their individual roles. ▶

▶ **Competence**

- Address training issues through toolbox talks, instruction or coaching.
- Consider how the competence of the contractor will be verified:
  - Can they demonstrate previous health and safety performance, eg references/pre-qualification questionnaire?
  - Can they verify health and safety training?
  - Can verification of licensing be obtained where required, eg Gas Safe registration?
- Will the contractor's lack of experience within your organisation lead to additional risks? If so, how will this be addressed?

Co-operation

What is worker involvement?

This means involvement of the workforce beyond the required legal minimum standard (ie more than consultation), where you develop a genuine management/workforce partnership based on trust, respect and co-operation.

With such a partnership in place, a culture can evolve in which health and safety problems are jointly solved and in which concerns, ideas and solutions are freely shared and acted upon.

The effect of workforce involvement is that operational practices and health and safety risk management are aligned for the benefit of all and with the co-operation of everyone (workers, their representatives and managers). The advice on pages 12–13 will help you decide if you are doing what you need to.

Co-ordination with contractors

The second aspect of co-operation is co-ordination with contractors (see pages 25–6), as well as others in an organisation's supply chain.

As health and safety affects the entire workforce of an organisation, it makes sense for all workers to be involved in managing health and safety.

Ways of involving workers

Involving workers is key to integrating health and safety as part of everyday business rather than being seen as something done by somebody else.

Organisations can find appropriate ways to involve their workers in managing health and safety. For smaller firms, this may be simply:

- encouraging open communications (eg toolbox talks, suggestion schemes, notice boards, or health and safety walkabouts) where workers can discuss or raise their concerns;
- giving recognition when workers identify risks.

For larger businesses, more formal health and safety forums or committees can be a means of enabling worker involvement which may need to cater for part-time workers and contractors.

Contacts with external services

Employers need to ensure that any necessary contacts with external services are arranged, and procedures are put in place so workers know what to do in situations presenting serious and imminent danger, such as a fire.

You need to have effective arrangements for first aid, emergency medical care and rescue work. This may only mean making sure that workers know the necessary telephone numbers and, where there is a significant risk, they are able to contact any help they need.

Contacts and arrangements with external services should be recorded, and should be reviewed and revised as necessary.

Shared workplaces

Where a number of employers share a workplace and their workers face the same risks, one employer should arrange contacts on behalf of themselves and the other employers.

High-hazard or complex workplaces

In high-hazard or complex workplaces, employers should designate appropriate staff to routinely contact the emergency services and utilities.

They should provide enough information for those services and utilities to take appropriate action in emergencies, including those likely to happen outside normal working hours.

Emergency procedures

Employers must explain clearly the procedure for any worker to follow in serious and imminent danger.

Employees and others at work need to know when they should stop work and how they should move to a place of safety. In some cases this will require full evacuation of the workplace, in others it might mean some or all of the workforce moving to a safer part of the workplace.

Emergency planning and co-operation with the emergency services

Police officers, fire-fighters and other emergency service workers, for example, may sometimes need to work in circumstances of serious or imminent danger in order to fulfil their commitment to the public. The procedures should reflect these responsibilities, and the time delay before such workers can move to a place of safety.

Work should not be resumed after an emergency if a serious danger remains. If there are any doubts, expert assistance should be sought, eg from the emergency services and others.

Danger areas

A danger area is a work environment where the level of risk is unacceptable, but an employee must enter without taking special precaution. Such areas are not necessarily static, in that minor alterations or an emergency may convert a normal working environment into a danger area.

The hazard involved need not occupy the whole area (as in the case of a toxic gas) but can be localised, eg where there is a risk of an employee coming into contact with bare, live electrical conductors. The area must be restricted to prevent inadvertent access.

Exceptional circumstances for re-entering danger areas

For emergency service workers there may be circumstances when re-entering serious danger areas may be deemed necessary, for example where human life is at risk.

When such exceptional circumstances can be anticipated, the procedures should set out the special protective measures to be taken (and the pre-training required), as well as the steps needed to authorise such actions.

Principles that help clarify how Fire and Rescue Authorities can strike the balance between their operational and health and safety duties are set out in an HSE publication at www.hse.gov.uk/services/fire/duties.pdf.

Similarly, for police activities see HSE's website at: www.hse.gov.uk/services/police/duties.pdf.

This is expanded in an explanatory note: www.hse.gov.uk/services/police/explanatory-note.pdf.

Find out more

For more information on requirements to consult health and safety representatives and employees in existing health and safety legislation:

Consulting workers on health and safety. Safety Representatives and Safety Committees Regulations 1977 (as amended) and Health and Safety (Consultation with Employees) Regulations 1996 (as amended). Approved Codes of Practice and guidance L146 (Second edition) HSE Books
ISBN 978 0 7176 6461 0
www.hse.gov.uk/pubns/books/l146.htm

HSE's worker involvement site:
www.hse.gov.uk/involvement

Consulting employees on health and safety: A brief guide to the law Leaflet INDG232(rev2)
HSE Books www.hse.gov.uk/pubns/indg232.htm

HSE guidance for the Police Service:
www.hse.gov.uk/services/police

HSE guidance for the Fire and Rescue Services:
www.hse.gov.uk/services/fire

Key actions in co-operating effectively

Leaders

- Gain commitment from your managers to consult and involve the workers.
- Show commitment to involving workers by being visible, communicating and listening to concerns, and jointly solving problems.
- Allocate resources to allow effective consultation to take place.
- Discuss with employees and representatives the best ways for information to be shared (www.hse.gov.uk/involvement/involveemployees.htm). Consider issues of language, literacy and learning disabilities if appropriate.

Managers

- Find out how your workers want to be consulted. How you consult will be affected by:
  - the size and structure of your organisation;
  - the diversity of your workforce;
  - the type of work carried out;
  - trade union representation;
  - people who work offsite;
  - the nature of the risks present.
- Think about how you will share information – remember to consider contractors and those who may have language barriers.
- By law, you must consult your workforce about any change that may substantially affect their health and safety. Such changes may include:
  - new or different procedures;
  - types of work;
  - equipment;
  - premises;
  - ways of working, eg new shift patterns;
  - your arrangements for getting competent people (www.hse.gov.uk/involvement/competentperson.htm) to help you meet your obligations under health and safety laws, eg appointing a health and safety manager;
  - information you must give your workforce on the likely risks in their work and precautions they should take (www.hse.gov.uk/involvement/riskassessments.htm);
  - planning of health and safety training (www.hse.gov.uk/involvement/training.htm);
  - health and safety consequences of introducing new technology.
- Formulate plans to ensure the workforce is consulted (either directly or through their representatives) in good time on issues relating to their safety. This will mean workers feel health and safety is a part of normal work activity, not something that is left to 'specialists'.
- Decide what your procedure will be if there are disagreements.
- Have shift-workers and part-time workers been considered?
- Make sure you make contact with external services, if needed, when formulating your emergency procedures.

Competence

- Make sure you are familiar with the legal requirements to consult and involve workers (www.hse.gov.uk/involvement/whattoconsult.htm).
- Plan joint health and safety training sessions for managers and workers so they can share views and experiences.
- Managers should be confident about speaking to workers.
- If your workforce has appointed safety representatives, you must ensure they are provided with paid time off as is necessary to have training that enables them to carry out their role.
- Make sure workers know what to do in an emergency.

Communication

To achieve success in health and safety management, there needs to be effective communication up, down and across the organisation.

Organisations need to communicate information to their workers on the risk to their health and safety identified in their risk assessments, and the preventive and protective measures necessary to control risk.

The information provided should be communicated appropriately, taking into account:

- workers' levels of competence;
- the size and structure of the organisation.

How size and structure affect communication

A high-risk workplace, with a large unionised workforce spread over multiple sites, may have trade union representatives from different sites as members of a formal health and safety committee that meets regularly, and feeds into a corporate health and safety committee.

A non-unionised, smaller workplace located on one small, low-risk site, is more likely to consult directly with employees on a day-to-day basis (eg through toolbox talks, or short safety briefings).

Find out more

Consulting and involving your workers – ways to engage: www.hse.gov.uk/involvement/factorstoconsider.htm

More advice on human factors: www.hse.gov.uk/humanfactors/topics/culture.htm

HSE human factors briefing note on safety-critical communications: www.hse.gov.uk/humanfactors/topics/08communications.pdf

HSE human factors guide on common topics in safety-critical communications: www.hse.gov.uk/humanfactors/topics/common3.pdf

Key actions in communicating effectively

Leaders

- Ensure that time is allocated so that communications can take place.

Managers

- Formulate plans for cascading information. Remember to plan how you will get messages across to contractors, anyone with low levels of literacy, or those whose first language is not English.
- Think about what needs to be communicated and to whom. How will your health and safety policy, risk assessment findings and safe systems of work be shared?
- Lay out clear communications procedures for safety-critical tasks.
- Where needed, plan your communications with emergency services. Who will co-ordinate this and how will it be done?
- Ensure that communication is included in change management procedures.
- Ensure that written instructions are clear and up to date.
- Make sure that safety-critical messages have been given attention and are understood.

Worker consultation and involvement

- Involve workers or their representatives in planning communications activities. They will be able to help identify and resolve barriers to communication within your organisation.
- Are workers able to give feedback and report their concerns?
- Have you considered vulnerable groups within your workforce in your communications plans, eg young or inexperienced workers, workers with a disability or migrant workers?

Competence

- Plan training or coaching to ensure that line managers have the skills needed to carry out face-to-face discussions at all levels within the organisation.

Competence

Organisations must appoint one or more competent people to help carry out the measures needed to comply with the law. It is important for organisations to decide the level of competence necessary to comply with the law. A judgement can be made using the organisation's risk profile (see pages 21–4).

Who should be the competent person?

Smaller, low-hazard environments

The role could be allocated to the owner or someone else in the organisation who does not necessarily have a qualification but does have knowledge and experience of the business.

However, it is important that the nominated person is able to recognise issues outside their competence, so that more experienced advice can be sought where necessary.

Larger or more hazardous environments

The risk profile may point to employing a specialist adviser to comply with the law.

Find out more

HSE advice on competence in health and safety: www.hse.gov.uk/competence/

Competence-related guidance for a specific industry, task or working environment: www.hse.gov.uk/competence/industry-specific-competence.htm

Key actions in competence

Leaders

- Consider the organisation's risk profile and establish whether you have enough in-house competence to comply with your legal obligations. Plan ahead to ensure you retain enough experienced, competent employees.
- Ensure that workers and managers are able to deliver their responsibilities.
- Ensure that the nominated competent person(s) has time available to keep up to date with changes in the law and industry good practice.

Managers

- Carry out proper induction and reinforce learning through peer behaviour, coaching and supervision.
- Make sure all workers have the necessary training, knowledge and experience to carry out their job safely and without risk to their health.
- Make sure workers understand the information, instruction and training you are giving them, taking account of any language difficulties or disabilities. You may need to provide information in a language other than English.
- Consider workers' individual capability before allocating work. Will they have the capacity to react safely to circumstances or changes? If they are unable to do this, what might the consequences be?
- Set out arrangements to capture workers' ideas and suggestions.
- Make sure there are arrangements for retaining and sharing corporate knowledge.
- Identify workers with knowledge and experience who could help others develop their level of competence.
- Training alone does not achieve competence – make sure competence is achieved through consolidation and practical experience.
- Make sure human factors are covered, for example the effects of fatigue.

Worker consultation and involvement

- Encourage workers to identify gaps in their knowledge or experience.
- Discuss plans for learning and development with workers or their representatives.

Capabilities and training

What capabilities do employees need to have?

To comply with the law, employees need to have the skills, knowledge and experience to carry out their duties safely.

Organisations should take into account their employees' capabilities, to ensure the demands of the job do not exceed their ability to do the work without risk to themselves or others.

Everyone in an organisation requires adequate health and safety training. Training helps people gain the skills and knowledge, and ultimately the competence, to carry out their work safely and without risk to their health.

Training isn't just about formal 'classroom' courses – it can be delivered in a number of ways, for example:

- informal, 'on the job' training;
- written instructions;
- online information;
- simply telling someone what to do.

Employees must be given information about the risks involved in their work, and the steps that need to be taken to reduce or remove those risks.

Where training is particularly important

There are situations where health and safety training is particularly important, for example:

- when people are new to the job;
- on exposure to new or increased risks;
- where existing skills may have become rusty or need updating.

Training is not a substitute for risk control

Training should not be a substitute for proper risk control, for example to compensate for poorly designed equipment. It may be appropriate as a temporary measure of control until permanent improvements can be made.

Find out more

Health and safety training: A brief guide Leaflet INDG345(rev1) HSE Books www.hse.gov.uk/pubns/indg345.htm

Key actions in capability and effective health and safety training

Leaders

- Provide resources to enable training to take place. Ensure that sufficient time is given for training.
- Ensure a system is in place which provides assurance that workers and managers involved in safety-related work remain competent.
- Make sure that contingency plans are in place. What would happen if a key member of staff were to suddenly leave the organisation?
- Ensure that your organisation has access to competent health and safety advice. This may be through a trained in-house adviser, or a competent external consultant – see the Occupational Safety and Health Consultants Register (OSHCR): www.hse.gov.uk/oshcr.
- Demonstrate personal compliance with health and safety training. Workers will follow your example.

Managers

Planning for training

- Decide if training is necessary. Think about the job, the person who carries it out, the processes and equipment required.
- Remember that contractors will need to be trained.
- Ensure there is a system in place to identify training needs during recruitment and when there are changes of staff, plant, processes, substances or technology.
- Find out which specific training you must provide by law, such as for operating forklift trucks.
- Prioritise training needs. ▶

- Decide the format that training will take, for example:
  - formal course coaching;
  - informal, 'on the job' training;
  - written instructions;
  - online information;
  - simply telling someone what to do.
- Remember that additional arrangements may be necessary for those whose first language may not be English, or those with low levels of literacy.
- If the task is new, can you learn from other organisations?
- How will you make sure workers receive refresher training?
- Newly trained workers should receive close supervision to ensure that they are competent in carrying out their duties.

Monitoring and measuring training's effectiveness

- How will training records be kept?
- Monitor learning outcomes and training methods.
- Review training material regularly to ensure that it remains current.
- Consider remedial training if lack of competence is identified as the cause of an incident.
- Gather feedback on training.
- Decide whether the training delivered its objectives. Consider whether there have been any improvements following the training – if not, initiate changes.

Worker consultation and involvement

- You must consult workers or their representatives during the planning and organising of training.
- Appointed safety representatives must have paid time to carry out their functions, and to have training in those functions.

Competence

- Ensure that training material or information comes from a reliable source and that the person carrying out the training is competent to do so.
- If training is outsourced, make sure the trainer has a good understanding of your organisation and its requirements.
- Decide how the organisation will keep up to date with changes in legislation and methods of risk control.
- Remember that competence levels will drop if skills are not used on a regular basis – schedule refresher training at regular intervals.
- Simulation exercises and drills will be required for some high-risk activities, eg control room operators' full-site emergency exercises.
- Don't assume that workers will be competent following a course or instruction – check.
- Review your employees' capabilities and provide additional or refresher training if needed.

Specialist help

When you may need specialist help

You may need specialist help if your business has hazardous or complex processes. However, for many organisations a manager, leader, or competent member of staff should be able to take the necessary action to comply with the law.

See 'Find out more' on page 36 for other sources of information.

What the law says on specialist help

If you need to engage outside help, you must remember that you cannot devolve the management of health and safety risks to others. However, specialist or consultant help can be used to contribute to your overall health and safety management.

Using advisers does not absolve the employer from responsibilities for health and safety under the Health and Safety at Work etc Act 1974 and other relevant statutory provisions under the Regulatory Reform (Fire Safety) Order 2005 (www.hse.gov.uk/toolbox/fire.htm). It can only give added assurance that these responsibilities will be discharged adequately.

It is essential that the specialist or consultant is competent to provide your organisation with correct, proportionate advice.

Useful sources of advice may include:

- trade associations;
- safety groups;
- trade unions;
- consultants registered on the Occupational Safety and Health Consultants Register (OSHCR): www.hse.gov.uk/oshcr;
- local councils;
- health and safety training providers;
- health and safety equipment suppliers.

Additional checks for employing an occupational physician

If there is a need for medical support in the workplace it is not sufficient to engage any doctor. Specialist knowledge is required in occupational medicine – doctors with a Diploma in Occupational Medicine (DOccMed) are able to give basic advice with some understanding of main issues affecting work and health.

Members or Fellows of the Faculty of Occupational Medicine (MFOM or FFOM) have had in-depth training and are fully knowledgeable in occupational medicine (www.fom.ac.uk).

Associates of the Faculty of Occupational Medicine (AFOM) have core knowledge in occupational medicine, but are not specialists in this field (www.fom.ac.uk/membership/associate-afom).

Table 5 Some examples of specialist help

Specialist	Expertise
Ergonomists	■ Field of vision, sight lines ■ Manual handling/repetitive tasks ■ Workspace layout ■ Body size ■ Aspects of guarding and containment ■ Demands of tasks/equipment on people ■ The equipment used and whether it is appropriate for the task ■ Effects of the physical environment, including lighting, temperature and humidity on people ■ Issues of fatigue and opportunities/defences for human failure
Microbiologists	■ Assessment of biological hazards ■ Advice on risks and control measures to prevent or control health risks ■ Sampling for micro-organisms
Noise and vibration specialists	■ Measure levels ■ Advice on causes, elimination and practical solutions to reduce exposure
Occupational health professionals (doctors and nurses)	■ Diagnosis and treatment of work-related disease (doctors) ■ Assessment of risks to health and advice on managing those risks ■ Health surveillance and other health checks ■ Fitness-for-work issues ■ Advice on pre-employment health screening, sickness absence and ill-health retirement ■ Providing health education, advice on rehabilitation after illness or injury
Occupational hygienists	■ Assessment and practical advice on preventing or reducing health risks from chemical, biological and physical agents arising from work activities ■ Environmental monitoring
Physiotherapists	■ Provide treatment and rehabilitation advice ■ Advice on preventing musculoskeletal disorders
Radiation protection advisers	■ Advice on complying with legislation on the use of ionising radiation in the workplace ■ Conducting environmental monitoring
Specialist engineers	■ Advice on issues including control and instrumentation (C&I), electrical, chemical, mechanical engineering

Key actions in managing specialist help effectively

Leaders

- Make adequate resources available to provide competent advice to your organisation.
- Review the effectiveness of the arrangements for obtaining specialist help – poor or misinterpreted advice could have an adverse effect on your organisation.

Managers

- Think about exactly what you need help with.
- Make sure you have understood the advice given by the specialist, and that any solutions offered are sensible and workable.
- Implement the advice – monitor its effect and review.
- Meet with the specialist to discuss your requirements. It is essential that they have a good understanding of your organisation before offering advice.

Worker consultation and involvement

- Make sure the specialist or consultant works with workers or their representatives in assessing risk and establishing control measures.

Competence

- How will you check that the specialist is the right person to help?
- Do they have experience in your type of work?
- Have you checked that the specialist or consultant is competent? A good indicator is to check OSHCR (www.hse.gov.uk/oshcr).

Find out more

Institute of Occupational Safety and Health (IOSH):
www.iosh.co.uk

Royal Society for the Prevention of Accidents (RoSPA):
www.rospa.com

British Safety Council (BSC):
www.britsafe.org

Competence in health and safety:
www.hse.gov.uk/competence

National Examination Board for Occupational Safety and Health (NEBOSH):
www.nebosh.org.uk

Trades Union Congress (TUC):
www.tuc.org.uk

Federation of Small Businesses (FSB):
www.fsb.org.uk

Chartered Institute of Environmental Health (CIEH):
www.cieh.org

Royal Society of Chemistry (RSC):
www.rsc.org

EEF – The Manufacturers' Organisation:
www.eef.org.uk

BOHS (The Chartered Society for Worker Health Protection): www.bohs.org

Implementing your plan

In addition to ensuring everyone is competent to carry out their work safely, and that there is adequate supervision to make sure arrangements are followed, workplace precautions will be easier to implement if:

- risk control systems and management arrangements have been well designed;
- those systems and arrangements recognise existing business practice and human capabilities and limitations.

The key steps

- Decide on the preventive and protective measures needed and put them in place.
- Provide the right tools and equipment to do the job and keep them maintained.
- Train and instruct, to ensure everyone is competent to carry out their work.
- Supervise to make sure that arrangements are followed.

Documentation

Documentation on health and safety should be functional and concise, with the emphasis on its effectiveness rather than sheer volume of paperwork.

Focusing too much on the formal documentation of a health and safety management system will distract you from addressing the human elements of its implementation – the focus becomes the process of the system itself rather than actually controlling risks.

In some cases, the law requires suitable records to be maintained, eg a record of risk assessments under the Management of Health and Safety at Work Regulations 1999 (MHSWR) and the Control of Substances Hazardous to Health Regulations 2002 (COSHH) – see 'Find out more' below.

Implementing risk control plans

The control of relatively minor risks affecting all employees (such as ensuring passages and gangways remain free from obstruction) can be dealt with by a number of simply stated general rules.

The control of more hazardous activities may need more detailed risk control systems. The control of high-hazard activities may demand detailed workplace precautions and a risk control system that needs to be strictly followed, such as a permit-to-work system.

The type, frequency and depth of maintenance activities should reflect the extent and nature of the hazards and risks revealed by risk assessment. The balance of resources devoted to the various risk control systems will also reflect your risk profile (see pages 21–4).

Find out more

Management of Health and Safety at Work Regulations: www.legislation.gov.uk/uksi/1999/3242/contents/made

Control of substances hazardous to health. The Control of Substances Hazardous to Health Regulations 2002 (as amended). Approved Code of Practice and guidance L5 (Sixth edition)
HSE Books ISBN 978 0 7176 6582 2
www.hse.gov.uk/pubns/books/l5.htm

Key actions in implementing your plan effectively

Leaders

- Leaders should take positive steps to address human factors issues and to encourage safe behaviour. They need to recognise that the prevailing health and safety culture is a major influence in shaping people's safety-related behaviour.
- Make the necessary resources available to successfully implement your plan. Resources include human resources and specialised skills, organisational infrastructure, technology and financial resources.

Managers

- Keep any documentation proportionate to the complexity of the risks concerned. Keep it to the minimum needed for effectiveness and efficiency.
- Agree realistic timescales for implementation of any plans with your workforce.
- Ensure all concerned are clear on their role and responsibilities, and understand the steps they need to undertake to meet the objectives. Clearly communicate who is responsible, accountable and competent to undertake specific tasks.
- Demonstrate your commitment to delivery at all levels within the organisation, using a variety of communication channels to engage your workforce in implementation. This can be through visible behaviour, written material and face-to-face discussions.
- Keep people informed of progress and maintain a focus in the key risks and issues. Use review meetings (or make use of existing internal forums) as a basis for helping to make further improvements.
- Measure progress of implementation against clear milestones or performance indicators and make necessary adjustments if there is early evidence that requirements are not being met.
- Recognise contributions and safe behaviours that help create or reinforce positive attitudes and behaviours.
- Do your arrangements give you the assurance that workers and contractors are following workplace precautions and risk controls?
- Make full use of expertise available on safety committees and other forums (where these are in place) to deliver.

Worker consultation and involvement

- Involve and consult workers and representatives throughout any implementation, by ensuring you have systems in place that allow workers to raise concerns and make suggestions, eg staff suggestion schemes, online communities, committees etc.
- Make sure you consider all feedback, take action or provide a prompt response.

Competence

- Ensure the competence of individuals is developed through experience and training, managers are providing coaching and the organisation learns by making use of specialist advice as required.
- Use the results of progress reviews to feed into future training plans – this helps with continuous improvement and avoids complacency.

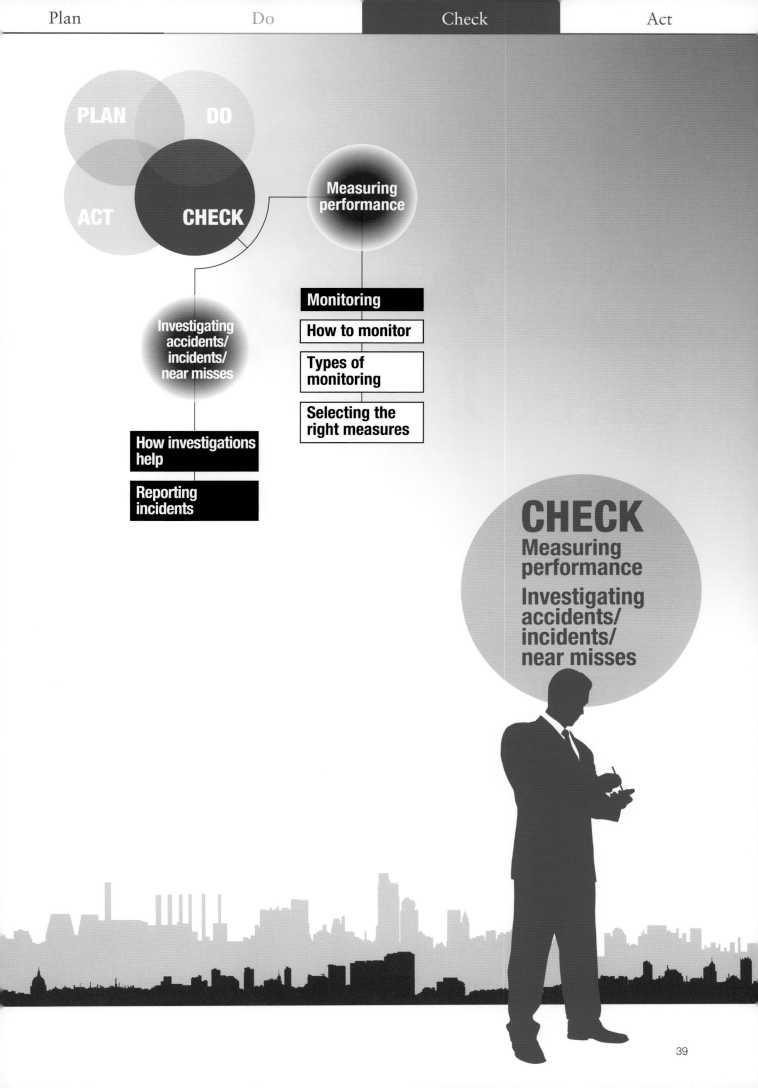

PLAN

DO

ACT

CHECK

Measuring performance

Monitoring

How to monitor

Types of monitoring

Selecting the right measures

Investigating accidents/ incidents/ near misses

How investigations help

Reporting incidents

CHECK
Measuring performance

Investigating accidents/ incidents/ near misses

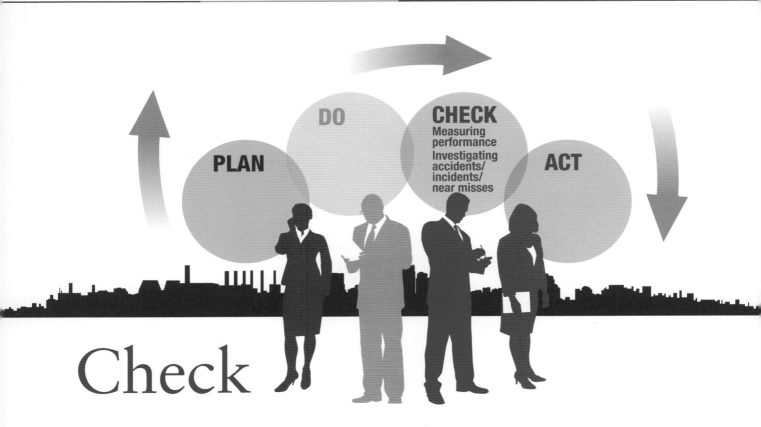

Check

Monitoring and reporting are important parts of health and safety arrangements. Management systems allow organisations to receive both specific (eg incident-led) and routine reports on the performance of health and safety policy.

- **Measuring performance**
  - Make sure that your plans have been implemented – 'paperwork' on its own is not a good performance measure.
  - Assess how well the risks are being controlled and if you are achieving your aims. In some circumstances formal audits may be useful.
- **Investigating accidents and incidents**
  - Investigate the causes of accidents, incidents or near misses.

Measuring performance

Checking that you are managing risks in your organisation is a vital, sometimes overlooked step. It will give you the confidence that you are doing enough to keep on top of health and safety and maybe show you how you could do things better in the future.

Checking involves setting up an effective monitoring system, backed up with sensible performance measures.

Investigating and analysing incidents will also make a big contribution to understanding health and safety in your business (see pages 43–4).

Monitoring

You need to be sure that your monitoring adds value and isn't just a tick-box exercise.

Good-quality monitoring will not just identify problems but will help you understand what caused them and what sort of changes are needed to address them. Poor monitoring might tell you that something is wrong but may not help you understand why, or what to do about it.

How to monitor

Use the same approach to monitor your health and safety performance as you would when you monitor other aspects of your business.

Monitoring requires time and effort. So you need to allocate appropriate resources and possibly train staff involved in it ahead of time. Businesses may monitor health and safety in different ways, depending on size and sector, but there are some basic principles that apply across the board.

Monitoring needs to be timely. As with all other business systems, you want to know what is happening in your organisation at the moment rather than at some point in the past.

The outcome of your monitoring will have most impact if it is reported back to key decision makers in your organisation. Unless there's a board-level commitment in advance, so you can act on what your monitoring tells you, then all your efforts to collect information could be wasted.

Types of monitoring

There are many different types of monitoring but they can generally be categorised as either 'active' or 'reactive':

- **Active methods** monitor the design, development, installation and operation of management arrangements. These tend to be preventive in nature, for example:
  - routine inspections of premises, plant and equipment by staff;
  - health surveillance to prevent harm to health;
  - planned function check regimes for key pieces of plant.
- **Reactive methods** monitor evidence of poor health and safety practice but can also identify better practices that may be transferred to other parts of a business, for example:
  - investigating accidents and incidents (see pages 43–4);
  - monitoring cases of ill health and sickness absence records.

Selecting the right measures

Most organisations use performance measures as part of their monitoring. Checking performance against a range of pre-determined measures is one of the most frequently used techniques of monitoring.

Selecting the right measures to use is the critical step. Using the wrong measures will cause a lot of unnecessary and unproductive effort, with little benefit to your organisation.

Key actions in measuring performance effectively

Leaders

- Demonstrate commitment to the process.
- Ensure that systems are in place to report performance upwards so that you, as leaders or directors, can review and be assured that legal compliance is achieved and maintained.
- Make certain there is a process in place to report serious incidents upwards immediately.
- Receive and review reports at regular intervals.
- Question results and ensure that action is planned to tackle poor performance and ensure the system you use to manage health and safety works.

Managers

Think about who will monitor what
- You may need to involve different levels within the management chain, as well as workers' representatives and health and safety advisers.

Decide how often monitoring will take place
- Be proportionate.
- Think about your risk profile.
- Monitor key risks and precautions more often and in more detail.
- Remember that the frequency of some monitoring or inspections is determined by law.

Plan what action you will take if your measure goes up or down
- There's no use getting information about performance if you haven't got some idea of what you will do if performance looks like it needs to improve.

Use performance measurement results
- To improve health and safety performance.
- To learn from human and organisational failures.
- To share lessons learned within your own organisation and with other organisations.

Review your performance measures every so often against your policy
- Changes in your business could mean that existing performance measures are out of date.
- You may also find the measures you've chosen don't help you understand how well you're managing health and safety. In these circumstances, you will need to update your approach.

For sites with major-accident hazards, focus on performance measures for critical activities or plant
- Safety-critical tasks with much human interaction.
- Operational performance of safety-critical devices, eg relief valves.

Worker consultation and involvement

- Involve your workforce in setting and monitoring your health and safety performance measures.
  - Workers may have important information as to which measures make the difference when it comes to risk.
- Involve everyone in the monitoring process.
  - Encourage workers to monitor their own work area, reporting any issues they observe.
  - Make reports available to everyone within the organisation.

Competence

- Use the results of monitoring to feed into future training plans.

Investigating accidents and incidents

In any business or organisation things don't always go to plan. You need to prepare to deal with unexpected events in order to reduce their consequences. Workers and managers will be more competent in dealing with the effects of an accident or emergency if you have effective plans in place that are regularly tested.

You should monitor and review any measures you have put in place to help control risk and prevent accidents and incidents from happening. Findings from your investigations can form the basis of action to prevent the accident or incident from happening again and to improve your overall risk management. This will also point to areas of your risk assessments that need to be reviewed.

An effective investigation requires a methodical, structured approach to information gathering, collation and analysis.

Why investigate?

- Health and safety investigations form an essential part of the monitoring process that you are required to carry out. Incidents, including near misses, can tell you a lot about how things actually are in reality.
- Investigating your accidents and reported cases of occupational ill health will help you uncover and correct any breaches in health and safety legal compliance you may have been unaware of.
- The fact that you thoroughly investigated an incident and took remedial action to prevent further occurrences would help demonstrate to a court that your company has a positive attitude to health and safety.
- Your investigation findings will also provide essential information for your insurers in the event of a claim.

An investigation can help you identify why the existing risk control measures failed and what improvements or additional measures are needed. It can:

- provide a true snapshot of what really happens and how work is really done (workers may find short cuts to make their work easier or quicker and may ignore rules – you need to be aware of this);

- improve the management of risk in the future;
- help other parts of your organisation learn;
- demonstrate your commitment to effective health and safety and improving employee morale and thinking towards health and safety.

Investigating near misses and undesired circumstances, where no one has been harmed, is as useful as, and may be easier than, investigating accidents.

In workplaces where a trade union is recognised, appointed health and safety representatives have the right to:

- investigate potential hazards and dangerous occurrences in the workplace;
- examine causes of workplace accidents.

Reporting incidents

All employers, the self-employed and people in control of work premises have duties under the Reporting of Injuries, Diseases and Dangerous Occurrences Regulations (RIDDOR).

They must report certain work-related injuries, cases of ill health and dangerous occurrences. RIDDOR applies to all work activities but not all incidents are reportable.

Reporting incidents should not stop employers undertaking their own investigation to ensure risks are controlled effectively.

Further information about what must be reported and how to report it can be found on HSE's RIDDOR site (see below).

Find out more

Investigating accidents and incidents: A workbook for employers, unions, safety representatives and safety professionals HSG245 HSE Books
ISBN 978 0 7176 2827 8
www.hse.gov.uk/pubns/books/hsg245.htm

HSE's RIDDOR website: www.hse.gov.uk/riddor

Key actions in effective accident/incident investigation

Leaders

- Verify that plans are in place to deal with immediate risks following unforeseen events.
- Make sure there is a reporting process so that leaders are informed of accidents, incidents or cases of occupational ill health.
- Consider lessons from the accident/incident history of others in similar industries or organisations – could the same mistakes be avoided?
- Ensure that people are held to account if failings reoccur.

Managers

- Formulate plans:
  - What must workers report?
  - How will reporting procedures be communicated to workers?
  - How will work-related ill health, accidents or near misses be notified?
  - Who will assist in the investigation?
  - What action will be taken as a result?
  - How will you identify trends?
- Ensure reporting procedures are suitable and workable.
- Examine all incident/accident/near-miss reports and identify trends.
- Be proportionate in any investigation, according to the level of risk identified. Establish what happened, when, where and why. Collect evidence:
  - consider what the evidence shows;
  - compare what you have found against industry standards/HSE guidance etc.
- Investigate accidents with a high priority – before people's memories fade and while evidence is still available.
- Look at root or underlying issues, not just immediate causes:
  - immediate causes – premises, plant and substances, procedures, or people;
  - underlying causes – management arrangements and organisational factors such as design, selection of materials, maintenance, management of change, adequacy of risk controls, communication, competence etc.
- Record and keep findings:
  - They may be required later in a formal investigation or legal proceedings.
- Engage specialist help to support complex investigations, eg an operation involving major accident hazards.

Worker consultation and involvement

- Involve workers or their representatives in the planning process and in the target-setting process.
- Carry out joint investigation with workers' representatives.
- Involve workers or their representatives in monitoring performance.

Competence

- Consider how competency is achieved, tested and maintained.
- Do investigators have the necessary training, knowledge and experience to carry out their duties?
- Consider whether training issues contributed to causes of accidents/incidents/near misses.
- Seek specialist advice if needed.

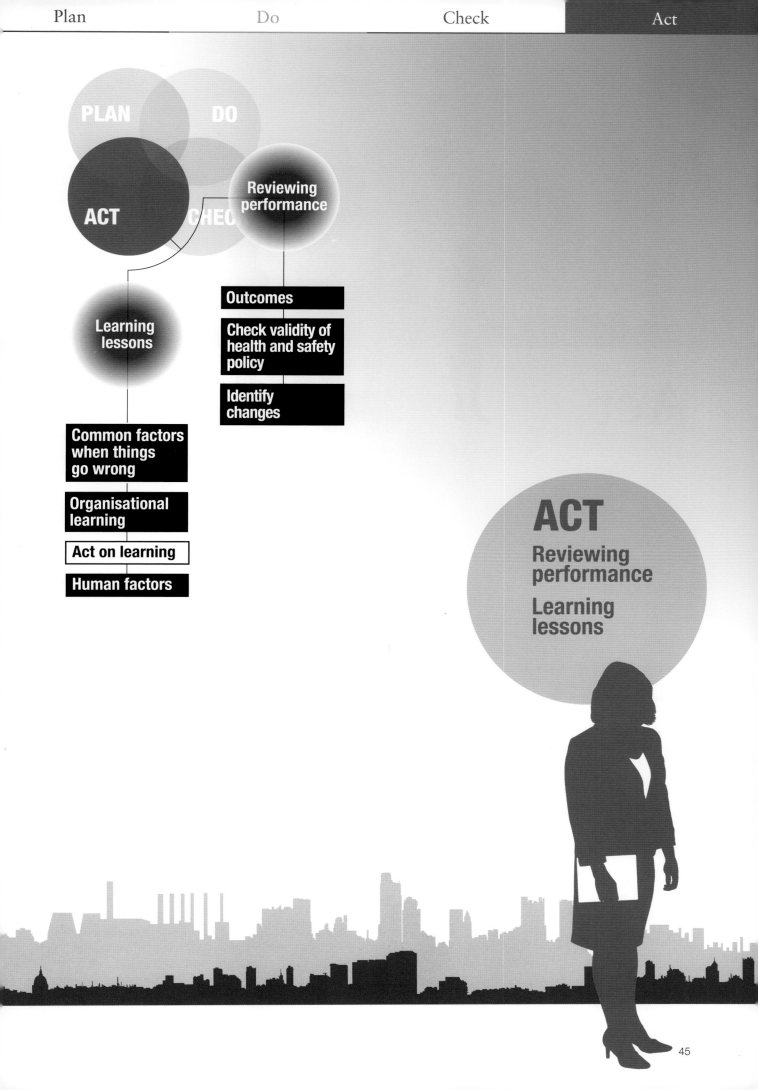

PLAN
DO
ACT
CHECK

Reviewing
performance

Learning
lessons

Outcomes

Check validity of
health and safety
policy

Identify
changes

Common factors
when things
go wrong

Organisational
learning

Act on learning

Human factors

ACT
**Reviewing
performance**

**Learning
lessons**

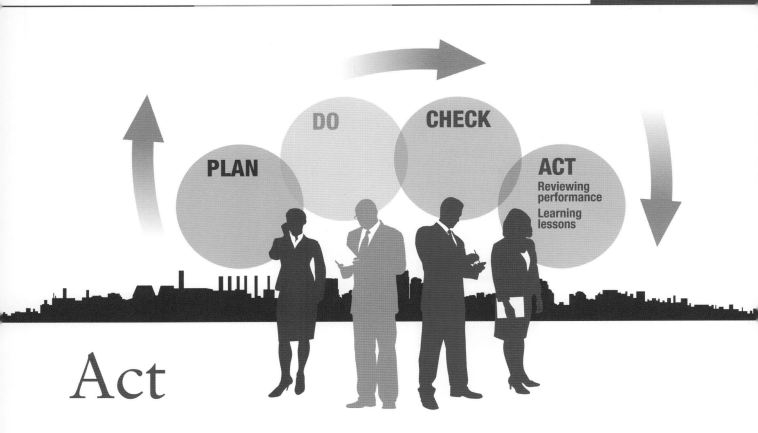

Act

It is important that organisations review their health and safety performance.

It allows you to establish whether the essential health and safety principles – effective leadership and management, competence, worker consultation and involvement – have been embedded in the organisation. It tells you whether your system is effective in managing risk and protecting people.

- **Review your performance**
  - Learn from accidents and incidents, ill-health data, errors and relevant experience, including from other organisations.
  - Revisit plans, policy documents and risk assessments to see if they need updating.
- **Take action on lessons learned**
  - Include audit and inspection reports.

Reviewing performance

Carrying out reviews will confirm whether your health and safety arrangements still make sense. For example, you'll be able to:

- check the validity of your health and safety policy;
- ensure the system you have in place for managing health and safety is effective.

You'll be able to see how the health and safety environment in your business has changed. This will enable you to stop doing things that are no longer necessary while allowing you to respond to new risks.

Reviewing also gives you the opportunity to celebrate and promote your health and safety successes. Increasingly, third parties are requiring partner organisations to report health and safety performance publicly.

The most important aspect of reviewing is that it closes the loop. The outcomes of your review become what you plan to do next with health and safety.

Key actions in reviewing performance effectively

Leaders

- Consider the review findings. If improvement is needed act now, rather than reacting to an incident in the future.
- Make sure the review is carried out according to the plans, and that a report is issued to senior leaders at least annually.
- Ensure the scope of the review will give assurance that risks are as low as reasonably practicable (see page 20), and that your organisation is complying with health and safety law.

Managers

What are the objectives of the review?
- Making judgements about the adequacy of health and safety performance
- Assurance that the system for managing health and safety is working
- Ensuring you are complying with the law
- Setting standards
- Improving performance
- Responding to change
- Learning from experience

Who will carry out the review?
- Someone independent, perhaps from another business area, could add value to the process.

What type of information will be collected?
- Active monitoring (before things go wrong)
- Reactive monitoring (after things go wrong)
- Accident/incident/near-miss data
- Training record
- Inspection reports
- Investigation reports
- Risk assessments
- New guidance
- Issues raised by workers or their representatives
- Checks required by law, eg on lifting equipment and pressure systems

How often will you need to carry out a review?
- This will depend on your risk profile (see pages 21–4).

Think about the supply chain
- How could the actions or health and safety performance of suppliers or contractors affect your organisation?

Consider incidents that have occurred in similar organisations
- Could they be repeated in your organisation?

Report the review findings
- It is crucial that you report any findings to everyone within the organisation.

Ensure remedial actions have been carried out
- You also need to make sure that the measures work.

Worker consultation and involvement

- Discuss plans for review with workers or their representatives.
- Use information from safety representatives' inspections to feed into review.
- Discuss the findings from your review with workers or their representatives – you will have more success in securing improvements if your workers are fully involved.

Competence

- Ensure that those carrying out the review have the necessary training, experience and good judgement to achieve competence in this task.
- See the section on 'Measuring performance' (pages 40–2) or use a trade association to assist with planning and benchmarking where you are now. Talk to similar organisations to compare performance and management practices.
- If risks are complex and could have serious consequences, consider getting specialist advice, or supporting one of your own workers by providing additional training.
- Check that training needs identified by the review have been addressed.

Learning lessons

Learning lessons involves acting on:

- findings of accident investigations and near-miss reports (see pages 43–4);
- organisational vulnerabilities identified during monitoring, audit and review processes.

Even in well-designed and well-developed management arrangements there is still the challenge of ensuring that all requirements are complied with consistently.

After an accident or case of ill health, many organisations find they already had systems, rules, procedures or instructions that would have prevented the event but were not complied with.

The underlying causes often lie in arrangements which are designed without taking proper account of human factors, or where inappropriate actions are condoned implicitly or explicitly by management action or neglect.

Common factors when things go wrong

Analysis of major incidents in high-hazard industries, with different technical causes and work contexts, has identified several common factors involved when things go wrong. These factors are related to:

- leadership;
- attitudes and behaviours;
- risk management and oversight.

When these aspects of an organisation become dysfunctional, important risks can become 'normalised' within it, leading to serious consequences.

Organisational learning

Organisational learning is a key aspect of health and safety management. If reporting and follow-up systems are not fit for purpose, for example if a blame culture acts as a disincentive to reporting near misses, then valuable knowledge will be lost.

If the root causes of precursor events are not identified and communicated throughout the organisation, this makes a recurrence more likely.

In many cases, barriers within an organisation – where different departments operate in 'silos' – inhibit organisational learning.

Human factors

Leaders and managers need to be aware of the people-related, cultural and organisational issues that may prevent lessons from being learned effectively in their organisations.

Find out more

HSE's human factors website: www.hse.gov.uk/humanfactors

Key actions in learning lessons effectively

Leaders and managers

- Show by your actions that safety is a core value.
- Promote a questioning attitude. Make sure you are not only receiving 'filtered good news' – do you welcome feedback and constructive challenge?
- Resolve ineffective procedures that result in 'workarounds' or violations of procedures.
- Be clear about your organisation's risk profile (see pages 21–4).
- Make sure your workers understand the risks that are being controlled.
- Avoid complacency – take responsibility for keeping your own knowledge and capability up to date.

Worker consultation and involvement

- Discuss plans with workers or their representatives.
- Avoid overburdening workers with initiatives.
- Involve workers in organisational change.

Competence

- Ensure that those providing top-level scrutiny have sufficient expertise to judge the importance of emerging health and safety issues and integrate those with other business decisions.
- Contractors must be competent and there should be checks in place to ensure they remain so.
- Take steps to avoid the loss of corporate memory.

Part 4: Resources

Leadership and management

HSE guidance on leading for health and safety and managing risk

Leading health and safety at work:
www.hse.gov.uk/leadership

Leadership for the major hazard industries: Effective health and safety management Leaflet INDG277(rev1) HSE Books www.hse.gov.uk/pubns/indg277.htm

Joint guidance with the Institute of Directors (IOD): *Leading health and safety at work: Leadership actions for directors and board members* Leaflet INDG417(rev1) HSE Books www.hse.gov.uk/pubns/indg417.htm

Risk management: www.hse.gov.uk/risk

Guidance for small and micro-businesses: *Health and safety made simple: The basics for your business* Leaflet INDG449 HSE Books
www.hse.gov.uk/pubns/indg449.htm
Microsite: www.hse.gov.uk/simple-health-safety

For businesses that need more detailed guidance: *The health and safety toolbox: How to control risks at work* HSG268 HSE Books ISBN 978 0 7176 6587 7
www.hse.gov.uk/pubns/books/hsg268.htm
Microsite: www.hse.gov.uk/toolbox

Writing a health and safety policy for your business: www.hse.gov.uk/simple-health-safety/write.htm

Management systems

The British Standards Institution produces internationally recognised standards, including BS OHSAS 18001 *Occupational health and safety management systems*: http://shop.bsigroup.com

The International Standards Organisation (ISO) develops and publishes international standards, including health-and-safety-related standards: www.iso.org/iso/home.htm

HSE and local authorities in Wales and South-West England produced a Management Assessment Tool for SMEs (MAST), for assessing health and safety management in small and medium-sized businesses: www.hse.gov.uk/foi/internalops/fod/inspect/mast

Institution of Occupational Safety and Health (IOSH) Risk Assessment Routefinder: www.ioshroutefinder.co.uk

Attitudes and behaviours

Reducing error and influencing behaviour HSG48 (Second edition) HSE Books
ISBN 978 0 7176 2452 2
www.hse.gov.uk/pubns/books/hsg48.htm

Measuring and reviewing performance

The Safety Climate Tool, published by the Health and Safety Laboratory (HSL), enables businesses to measure workforce attitudes to health and safety: www.hsl.gov.uk/products/safety-climate-tool.aspx

The Energy Institute (EI) Process Safety Survey is a process safety measurement and benchmarking tool, based on the Energy Institute's *High-level framework for process safety management*:
www.energyinst.org/eipss

EEF – The Manufacturers' Organisation – Health and Safety Balanced Scorecard:
www.eef.org.uk/members/healthandsafety/scorecard/about-the-scorecard/default.htm

SHEIIBA – Safety, Health, Environment Intra Industry Benchmarking Service: www.sheiiba.com

BSI Standards – self-assessment tool:
http://ohsonline.co.uk

RoSPA – Quality Safety Audit: www.rospa.com/consultancy/safetyaudits

Worker consultation and involvement

HSE guidance on worker consultation and involvement

How to involve workers in your business:
www.hse.gov.uk/involvement

Worker involvement – 'do your bit' guidance and workplace materials:
www.hse.gov.uk/involvement/doyourbit

Protecting migrant workers: www.hse.gov.uk/migrantworkers/employer/protecting.pdf

Other organisations that provide advice on consultation and involvement

The TUC produces guidance on workers' rights at work: www.tuc.org.uk

ACAS promotes employment relations and has produced the Model Workplace Toolkit that contains advice for managers: www.acas.org.uk

The following organisations conduct ballots, surveys and other ways of consulting employees, on behalf of businesses:

- Electoral Reform Services: www.erbs.co.uk
- Popularis: http://popularis.org
- IPA: www.ipa-involve.com

Competence

HSE guidance 'hub' on competence in health and safety: www.hse.gov.uk/competence

Competence-related guidance for a specific industry, task or working environment: www.hse.gov.uk/competence/industry-specific-competence.htm

Passport schemes for health and safety can be a useful way for employers to check that somebody working on their premises, or elsewhere doing work on their behalf, has received basic health and safety awareness training: www.hse.gov.uk/competence/health-and-safety-passport-schemes.htm

HSE produces a range of guidance on health and safety at work, organised by industry and topic: www.hse.gov.uk/guidance/industries.htm

Other organisations that provide advice on competence

The following organisations provide advice, guidance, training and/or qualifications to industry in the field of health and safety.

- The Health and Safety Laboratory (HSL) offers a range of training courses on health and safety-related topics: www.hsl.gov.uk/hsl-shop/health-and-safety-training-courses.aspx
- Chartered Institute of Environmental Health: www.cieh.org
- European Agency for Safety and Health at Work: https://osha.europa.eu/en

- Access Industry Forum: www.accessindustryforum.org.uk
- EEF – The Manufacturers' Organisation: www.eef.org.uk
- LANTRA: www.lantra.co.uk
- National Examination Board for Occupational Safety and Health (NEBOSH): www.nebosh.org.uk
- Institution of Occupational Safety and Health (IOSH): www.iosh.co.uk
- International Institute of Risk and Safety Management: www.iirsm.org
- Royal Society for the Prevention of Accidents (RoSPA): www.rospa.com
- British Safety Council: www.britsafe.org
- British Safety Industry Federation: www.bsif.co.uk
- Olympic Development Authority: http://learninglegacy.independent.gov.uk

Specialist advice

HSE specialist guidance

HSE publications: www.hse.gov.uk/pubns/books/

Getting specialist help with health and safety Leaflet INDG420(rev1) HSE Books www.hse.gov.uk/pubns/indg420.htm

Other organisations that may help provide businesses with specialist advice

- Occupational Safety and Health Consultants Register: www.oshcr.org
- British Psychological Society: www.bps.org.uk
- Human Factors and Ergonomics Society – European Chapter: www.hfes-europe.org
- BOHS (The Chartered Society for Worker Health Protection): www.bohs.org
- Chemical Hazards Communication Society: www.chcs.org.uk

Process safety

Guidance from HSE

Developing process safety indicators: A step-by-step guide for chemical and major hazard industries HSG254 HSE Books ISBN 978 0 7176 6180 0 www.hse.gov.uk/pubns/books/hsg254.htm

Leadership for the major hazard industries: Effective health and safety management Leaflet INDG277(rev1) HSE Books www.hse.gov.uk/pubns/indg277.htm

The Process Safety Leadership Group (PSLG) Final Report – *Safety and environmental standards for fuel storage sites* www.hse.gov.uk/comah/buncefield/fuel-storage-sites.pdf

PSLG Principles of Process Safety Leadership www.hse.gov.uk/comah/buncefield/pslgprinciples.htm

Guidance from the Organisation for Economic Co-operation and Development (OECD)

Guiding Principles for Chemical Accident Prevention, Preparedness and Response (2003) www.oecd.org

Addendum to Guiding Principles (2011) www.oecd.org

Corporate Governance for Process Safety: Guidance for senior managers in high-hazard industries (2012) www.oecd.org

Guidance from the Energy Institute (EI)

High-level framework for process safety management ('PSM framework'): www.energyinst.org/technical/PSM/PSM-framework

Human factors performance indicators for energy and related process industries: www.energyinst.org/hofpi

Other sources of information

- Center for Chemical Process Safety (CCPS): www.aiche.org/ccps
- Chemical Industries Association: www.cia.org.uk
- European Process Safety Centre: www.epsc.org

Further information

For information about health and safety, or to report inconsistencies or inaccuracies in this guidance, visit www.hse.gov.uk. You can view HSE guidance online and order priced publications from the website. HSE priced publications are also available from bookshops.

British Standards

British Standards can be obtained in PDF or hard copy formats from BSI: http://shop.bsigroup.com or by contacting BSI Customer Services for hard copies only Tel: 0845 086 9001 email: cservices@bsigroup.com.

The Stationery Office publications

The Stationery Office publications are available from The Stationery Office, PO Box 29, Norwich NR3 1GN Tel: 0870 600 5522 Fax: 0870 600 5533 email: customer.services@tso.co.uk Website: www.tsoshop.co.uk (They are also available from bookshops.) Statutory Instruments can be viewed free of charge at www.legislation.gov.uk, where you can also search for changes to legislation.

This guidance is available at: www.hse.gov.uk/pubns/books/hsg65.htm.